CW00672976

'If everything were to perish, all the books, monuments and photographs and only the woodcuts that he had executed in the ten years were spared, our whole present day world could be reconstructed from them'.   STEFAN ZWEIG

Frans Masereel (1889-1972) was a graphic artist of such astounding originality that he was revered not only by Zweig but by many other great writers of his time such as Hermann Hesse and Thomas Mann.

Masereel was born in Flanders but lived most of his life in France. Immensely prolific, he produced leaflets, posters and paintings and illustrated the works of Tolstoy, Rolland, Zola and Wilde as well as promoting the Spanish Republican cause. But it is his novels-without-words that have assured him international immortality. The woodcut cycles in which the story unfolds through pictures alone, are symbolic mirrors of civilization in which, as Mann wrote, he depicted *'the brutal factory of modern life'.*

THE SUN explores man's fragile relationship with destiny, the dilemma of the individual struggling with his sense of collective purpose. The brilliant rays of the sun offer promise of liberty and progress. In his frenzied attempts to grasp the source of light, Masereel's hero undergoes a series of ever more dramatic adventures until he himself is consumed by the fireball, leaving the bewildered artist to ponder his fate. The poetic sadness of death is characteristically tempered by a strain of social optimism. As Hermann Hesse wrote of Masereel, *'He is essentially occupied with something totally timeless and eternal, with the eternally painful, eternally joyous, story of mankind.'*

FRANS MASEREEL

THE
SUN

A NOVEL TOLD IN 63 WOODCUTS

R

REDSTONE PRESS, LONDON

First UK edition
published in 1990 by
Redstone Press,
7a St Lawrence Terrace,
London W10 5SU.

Originally published as DIE SONNE by
Editions du Sablier, Geneva 1919

This edition published by arrangement
with Pantheon Books, USA

Woodcuts Frans Masereel © Europa Verlag Ag.

Designed by Julian Rothenstein
Printed and made in England

British Library Cataloguing in Publication data

Masereel, Frans, *1889-1972*
The Sun: 63 woodcuts
1. Belgian woodcuts. Masereel, Frans
1889-1972
1. Title 11. Die Sonne. *English*
769.924

ISBN 1 870003 85 3

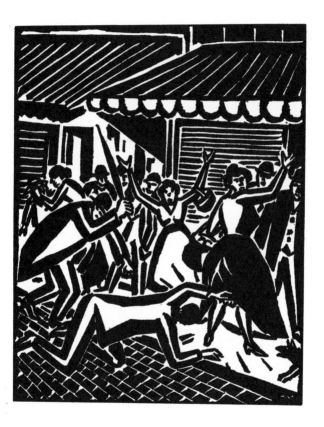